COLOR MY OW
ANIMAL
STORY

AN IMMERSIVE, CUSTOMIZABLE COLORING BOOK FOR KIDS
(THAT RHYMES!)

BRIAN C HAILES

For information about permission to reproduce selections from this book, please write Permissions, Epic Edge Publishing, 1934 Fielding Hill Ln, Draper, UT 84020.

www.epicedgepublishing.com

Library of Congress Cataloging-in-Publication Data
Color My Own Animal Story: An Immersive, Customizable Coloring Book for Kids (That Rhymes!)
Written by Brian C Hailes

p. cm.

Summary: Embark on a safari over the African savanna, an adventure through the jungles of South America, or visit your favorite farm staples in rural America—all in one immersive, customizable coloring activity storybook! And what will you find in these wild places? Animals! Lots and lots of animals! Mammals, reptiles, amphibians, birds and fish! The absolute color and diversity of the Animal Kingdom astounds! And it's all here, contained in this enjoyable bedtime story that your child can make their own, writing in their name and particulars, and coloring the illustrations themselves. Whether they love drawing, coloring, visiting zoos, the outdoors or just studying creatures of the wild from the air-conditioned comfort of home, these animals will pop from the pages and bring hours of excitement to your little animal expert—off of their screens and devices! And what a great little story! So climb a tree, jump in the water, or fly off your high perch to soar with the eagles, or just grab your crayons, markers and pencils and make this animal learning adventure your very own today!

(Intended for children ages 6-12 . . . or all kids at heart)

1. Childrens—Coloring Books. 2. Childrens—Animals
3. Childrens—Activity Books
II. Hailes, Brian C., ill. III. Title.

Paperback ISBN-13: 978-1-951374-49-5
Hardback ISBN-13: 978-1-951374-50-1

Printed in the USA
Designed by Epic Edge Publishing

10 9 8 7 6 5 4 3 2 1

Animals touch our souls in ways no human can.
— B.C. Hailes

COLOR MY OWN
ANIMAL STORY

AN IMMERSIVE, CUSTOMIZABLE COLORING BOOK FOR KIDS
(THAT RHYMES!)

STARRING: _____

The Animal Kingdom's here,

So young adventurers, let's explore!

But do take care, some creatures

May _____ , bite, peck, or roar!
(attack, pounce or charge)

Take it from a Toucan,

If you love to visit zoos,

The wild outdoors has much to offer

That's _____ and new . . .
(dangerous, marvelous or appealing)

The mighty Stag (or Buck to some),

Roams the wooded mountains;

It displays its _____ antlers,
(massive, hefty or fuzzy)

Living among _____, streams and fountains;
(trees, oaks or pines)

Usually a loner,

Unless _____ for a mate,
(fighting, searching or competing)

The male deer stakes its territory,

Before preparing to migrate . . .

The camouflaged Chameleon

Is one of nature's wonders;

It can catch _____ with its darting tongue,
(a fly, a bug or an insect)

And even change its own skin color!

Some Tree Frogs of the rainforest

Can also blend right in

With branches, leaves and foliage . . .

Or _____ out with a grin!
(stand, stick or hop)

The _____ Peacock fluffs its tail,
(lovely, handsome or colorful)

Awaiting a female's arrival;

Upon the beauty of its display

Rests the species' sole survival.

So it had better put on a

Grand, magnificent show;

For the _____ acceptance,
(lady's, female's or queen's)

That tail really needs to glow!

Southwestern Diamondbacks dance
To a tune their very own;
They slink and slither everywhere,
And they're usually alone . . .

But sometimes they will find a _____ ,
(pit, nest or den)
A so-called family of snakes;
Or merely act as roommates
With not hand, but fond tailshakes.

A baby Calf might bleat aloud,

Thirsty, calling for its mother;

Then _____ and compete for
(wrestle, wriggle or grapple)

Nice warm milk from Mother's udder.

Ponies, on the other hand,

Chase _____ in the fields;
(brothers, sisters or siblings)

Galloping and tackling . . .

And no one ever yields.

The long-haired, short-legged Yak

Hangs out in higher elevations;

They prefer it where it's _____ ,
(chilly, cooler or colder)

As they have for generations.

My fur would be the deepest _____ ,
(your favorite color)

If I happened to be a Yak;

I'd eat grass all day and get real fat;

Always down for a friendly chat.

Polar Bears love the Arctic cold,

With mountains of ice to roam;

Their thick white fur protects them

From their frosty, _____ home.
(frozen, beautiful or wonderful)

Meerkats, however, prefer the heat;

That warm, African sand;

They also like companionship . . .

And well-populate the land.

Back on the farm, the horse rears up,

If ever there's a threat;

Like a barking dog or _____ chicken,
(crazy, runaway or delinquent)

Or a visit to the vet.

Bulldogs too, will hold their ground,

And put on quite a show;

For any man or beast that _____,

(comes, approaches or trespasses)

It's not a friendly, "Hello."

In the deepest jungles of the south and east,

Tigers _____ and prowl;
(slink, lurk or skulk)

And Birds of Paradise dance and sing;

Deadly hunters and performing fowl.

Penguins of Antarctica,

Trek far to _____ their young
(birth, bear or deliver)

Through heavy, icy winds and cold,

Yet still find time for fun!

Sliding about on icy sheets

Into chilling waters deep,

They fish and splash and play and _____ ,
(gak, whoop or bark)

While their babies call and peep.

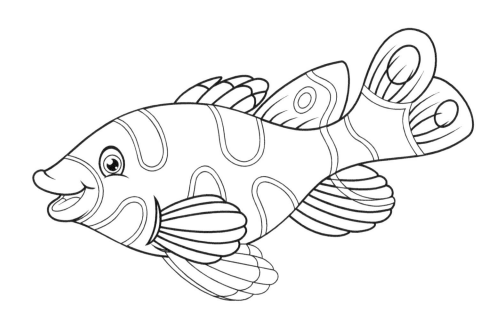

The long-necked Giraffe of the

Dry, African savanna;

Takes life easy, _____ and slow,
(calm, quiet or lazy)

Chewing leaves off the Acacia.

Monkeys in the treetops _____
(chitter, chatter or scream)

At nearly all the other creatures;

From branches, vines and treetrunks,

Like crazed fans filling the bleachers.

Apes and monkeys alike can vary

Drastically in their sizes,

But beware their teeth and _____ ,
(anger, strength or aggression)

And also, falling surprises!

The Leopard and the Cheetah,

Two of the kingdom's swiftest runners;

With their _____ , spotted coats,
(gorgeous, dazzling or elegant)

Nature's fashionista stunners!

The menacing, howling Gray Wolves,

Hunt in packs to catch their prey,

While minks, ferrets and _____ ,
(weasels, badgers or otters)

Split up and scatter, run astray.

With their long and slender bodies,

These small mammals also hunt;

Following their game into _____ ,
(holes, burrows or dens)

To catch, eat or confront!

This worldwide wildlife family,

Is truly _____ to behold!
(a wonder, a marvel or awesome)

Never stop exploring, and, like so many animals,

Be brave and bold!

THE END

OTHER "COLOR MY OWN" TITLES
NOW AVAILABLE!

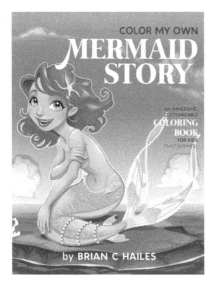

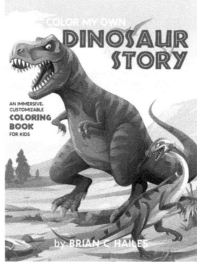

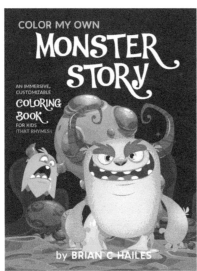

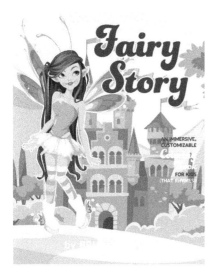

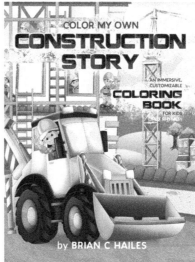

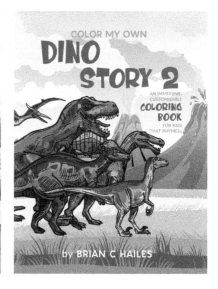

ABOUT THE AUTHOR

BRIAN C HAILES, creator of Draw It With Me (www.drawitwithme.com), is also the award-winning writer/ illustrator of over forty-five (and counting) novels, children's picture books, comics and graphic novels, including Blink: An Illustrated Spy Thriller Novel, Devil's Triangle, Dragon's Gait, Skeleton Play, Don't Go Near the Crocodile Ponds, If I Were a Spaceman, Here, There Be Monsters, Heroic, Passion & Spirit, Continuum (Arcana Studios), as well as McKenna, McKenna, Ready to Fly, and Grace & Sylvie: A Recipe for Family (American Girl), among others. In addition to his publishing credits, Hailes has also illustrated an extensive collection of fantasy, science fiction, and children's book covers as well as interior magazine illustrations. Hailes has received numerous awards for his works from across the country, including Winner of the L. Ron Hubbard Illustrators of the Future contest out of Hollywood. His artwork has also been featured in the 2017-2020 editions of Infected By Art.

Hailes studied illustration and graphic design at Utah State University where he received his Bachelor of Fine Arts degree, as well as the Academy of Art University in San Francisco.

He currently lives in Salt Lake City with his wife and four boys, where he continues to write, paint and draw regularly. More of his work can be seen at HailesArt.com

Other Titles Available from
Epic Edge Publishing

Illustrated Novels	Graphic Novels / Comics	Childrens Picture Books	Anthologies	Non-Fiction

Blink: An Illustrated Spy Thriller Novel
by Brian C Hailes

Avila
(Available 2021!)
by Robert J Defendi
& Brian C Hailes

Devil's Triangle: The Complete Graphic Novel
by Brian C Hailes
& Blake Casselman

Dragon's Gait
by Brian C Hailes

KamiKazi
by John English
& Brian C Hailes

If I Were a Spaceman: A Rhyming Adventure Through the Cosmos
by Brian C Hailes
& Tithi Luadthong

Here, There Be Monsters
by Brian C Hailes
& Tithi Luadthong

Don't Go Near the Crocodile Ponds
by Brian C Hailes

Skeleton Play
by Brian C Hailes

Can We Be Friends?
by Edie New
& Cindy Hailes

Cresting the Sun: A Sci-fi / Fantasy Anthology Featuring 12 Award-Winning Short Stories
by Brian C Hailes,
Rick Bennett
& Nicholas Adams

Heroic: Tales of the Extraordinary
by Blake Casselman,
David Farland,
Michael Stackpole
& more

Draw It With Me: The Dynamic Female Figure
(Available 2020!)
by Brian C Hailes

DIWM 2020 Annual 1
(Available 2020!)
by Brian C Hailes,
Heather Edwards
& more

Passion & Spirit: The Dance Quote Book
by Brian C Hailes

CPSIA information can be obtained
at www.ICGtesting.com
Printed in the USA
BVHW021645131220
595615BV00006B/334